The Lost Gift

by Elen Caldecott

Illustrated by Emma Levey

OXFORD

UNIVERSITY PRESS

In this story ...

Pip Squeak

Kit Bags

Pip and Kit run *Finders Squeakers* – a lost and found agency. They help return lost things to their owners.

Ria

Kit licked his lips. He was about to take a delicious bite of cake. Just then, the screen beeped.

"Sorry, Kit," Pip said. "It looks like we have a new mission. You can have your cake when we're finished."

"It's a <u>deal</u>!" said Kit.

Pip and Kit have made a <u>deal</u> that Kit can have his cake later. How do you think he feels about the <u>deal</u>?

A message appeared on the screen.

Help! I was on my way to my friend Sara's birthday party, and I left her gift on the bus. Please can you get it back before the party is over? Thank you, Ria.

Pip sent a message back. *We can help! Please send me Sara's address.*

Ria replied at once. *The party is at 12 Chestnut Street. The gift is on the number 7 bus.*

Why do you think Pip asked Ria to <u>send</u> her Sara's address?

Pip and Kit leaped on their motorbike and rode along the busy streets. They were <u>determined</u> to help Ria.

Pip stopped at the traffic lights. "Can you see the bus, Kit?" she asked.

"There's no sign of it," Kit replied.

Pip and Kit are <u>determined</u> to help. Does this mean that they have made up their minds to help or that they are still unsure what to do?

On the pavement nearby, a gull was pecking at some crumbs.

Kit had an idea. "Excuse me," he said to the gull. "We're looking for the number 7 bus. Can you help us?"

"Of course," the gull squawked.

The gull flapped her wings and took off. She flew high above them and gazed around. Then she swooped back down. "The bus is on Market Street," she said.

"Thank you!" Kit called.

"Hold on tight," Pip said to Kit. "I know a shortcut."

The motorbike zoomed forward. Pip raced along an alley.

"There's the bus!" Kit cried.

The bus had just driven past the end of the alley.

"We're going to catch it!" Pip shouted.

Just then, a huge lorry stopped. It blocked the end of the alley in front of them.

"Watch out!" Kit cried in <u>warning</u>.

Can you say "Watch out!" as if you were Kit, <u>warning</u> Pip of the danger?

Pip pulled sharply on the brakes, and the motorbike skidded to a halt.

"You can still catch up with the bus," squawked a voice.

Kit looked up. It was the gull!

"If you go through that archway you can get to the road by the market!" the gull said.

"Thanks again!" said Kit.

Pip drove to the market.

They saw a stall selling screws, nails and other bits and pieces. Pip stopped the motorbike and got off.

"Where are you going?" Kit asked. "We can't give up now. We need to get that gift back!"

"I'm not giving up," Pip replied. "I'm getting something to help us."

Pip went over to the stall. She bought something and slipped it into her backpack. Then she ran to the motorbike.

"You drive, Kit," she said. "I've got work to do."

"No problem," said Kit, with a <u>determined</u> expression on his face.

Kit revved the engine, and they set off again after the bus.

Can you show a <u>determined</u> expression like Kit's?

While Kit chased the bus, Pip was hard at work on her idea. She pulled everything she needed from her backpack and put the pieces together.

"Tah-dah!" she cried.

"Is that our grabbing tool?" Kit asked.

"Yes," Pip said, "but I've swapped the end of it for a magnet that I bought at the market."

Kit's eyes widened in astonishment. "Why did you do that?"

"You'll see!" Pip told him. "Just get us close to the bus."

They zoomed on, getting nearer and nearer to the bus.

Pip took careful aim with the grabbing tool. "This is my best <u>opportunity</u>!" she thought.

An <u>opportunity</u> is a good time to do something. Why is this the best <u>opportunity</u> for Pip to act?

Pip pressed the button. The magnet shot forward and stuck to the side of the bus – **THUNK!**

Pip let go of the button. She was pulled towards the bus!

Woo-hoo!

Right at the last moment, Pip let go of the handle. She flew through an open window and landed on a seat ... right next to the gift!
Pip picked it up and calmly rang the bell.

When the bus stopped, Pip hopped off.

Kit stopped beside her. "Can we make it to the party in time?" he asked.

"We can if we hurry!" Pip replied.

They raced towards Chestnut Street.

Pip placed the gift on Sara's doorstep, and Kit rang the doorbell. Then they ran and hid behind a wall.

Ria opened the door and smiled. "Sara, I've got something for you!" she called.

Back at the agency ...

Pip and Kit sat down to celebrate.

"We deserve some cake after all that racing about," Kit said.

Just then, the screen beeped.

"Sorry, Kit," said Pip. "We've got another situation to deal with!"

How did Pip and Kit save Ria from a difficult situation? What might have happened if they had not recovered the gift?

Read and discuss

Read and talk about the following questions.

Page 3: Do you think Pip will have to make a new <u>deal</u> with Kit at the end of the story?

Page 5: Can you describe some different ways you might <u>send</u> people messages?

Page 6: How does the story show that Pip and Kit were <u>determined</u> to get the gift back?

Page 10: Can you think of some signs you might see in school or in town that <u>warn</u> you of danger?

Page 18: How else could they have got the gift back, if Pip had missed her <u>opportunity</u> to get on the bus?

Page 23: Can you think of another <u>situation</u> that Pip and Kit might have to deal with?